Leo Has
Three Grandpas

...and they are all the best!

Leslye Alexander

Leo Has Three Grandpas

Copyright © 2022 by Leslye Alexander

First Edition

Hardcover ISBN: 979-8-88590-617-3
Paperback ISBN: 979-8-88590-618-0

I wish to thank the following people for their assistance and support during my first experience of writing and publishing this book:

Susan Vazquez
Brad Alexander
Jill Alexander
Rose Ross

This book is dedicated
to my grandson Leo
and to all grandpas

Hi! My name is Leo and today for Show and Tell I would like to tell my whole class about my three grandpas.

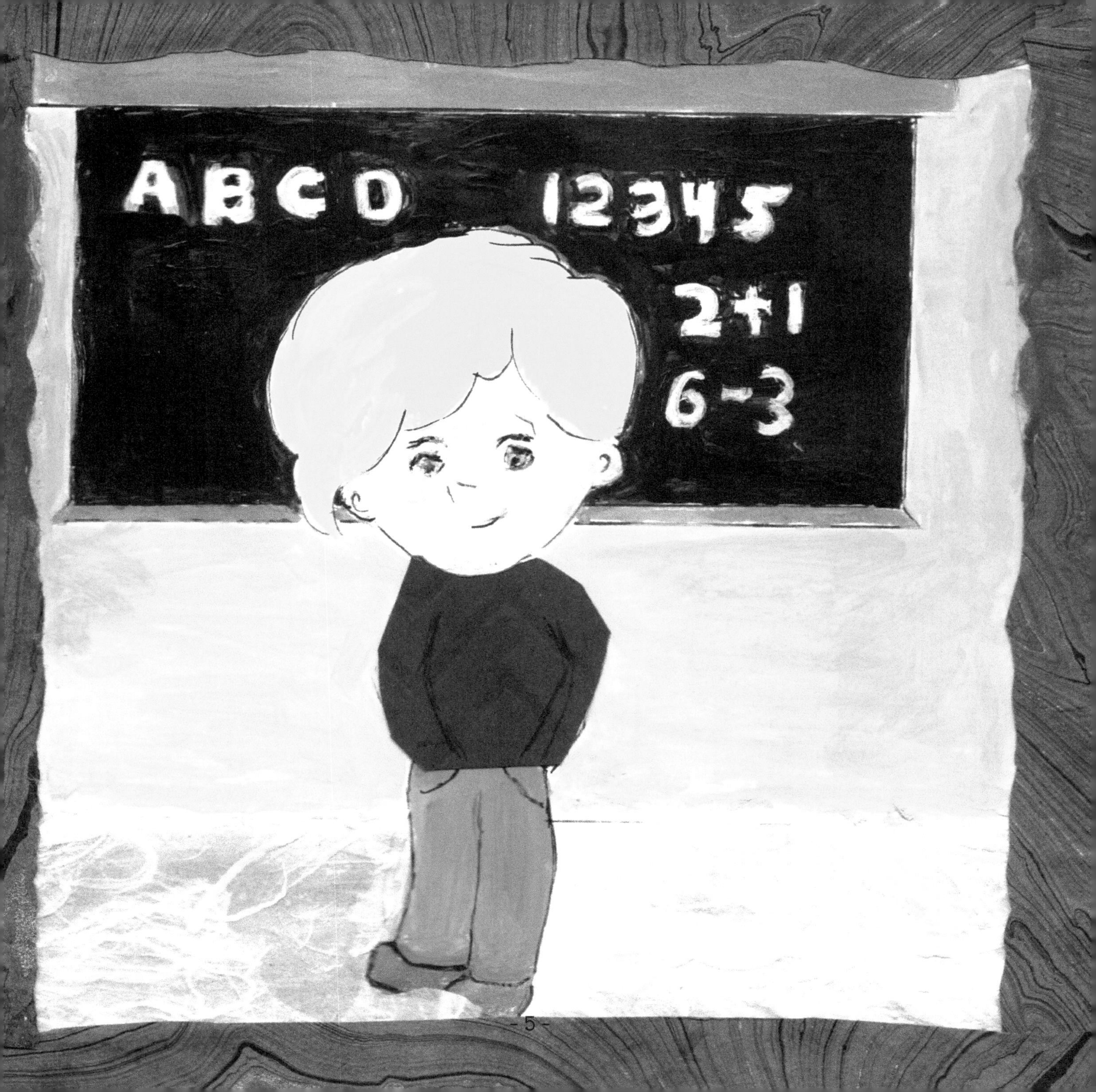
ABCD 12345
2+1
6-3

Grandpa Number One is named Grampy. And that's what I call him because that's his name.

Grampy is my daddy's daddy.

Grampy is a dentist, so he makes sure that everyone takes care of their teeth. And when I visit Grampy's office, I sit in his big chair, and he looks in my mouth and checks all of my teeth.

Grampy wants everyone to brush and floss. So when I am home, I brush and floss my teeth every morning and every night.

He is a really good dentist.

When Grampy is not working, he calls me on the phone and says, "Hi, Leo. It's Grampy, and I am coming to visit you."

And you know what?

He drives on a big highway to come and play with me.

We go to the park, and Grampy swings me super high on the swings.

It is so awesome!

But you know what else?

Sometimes when it's warm outside, Grampy plays golf with his friends. And he lets me watch.

And guess what. Grampy says he will teach me how to play golf when I get bigger.

Grandpa Number Two is named Pop-Pop. Pop-Pop is married to my grammy, who is Daddy's mother.

Pop-Pop is very, very tall, so I have to look all the way up to see him.

Pop-Pop works in an airplane and travels to so many faraway places. He told me that someday he will take me on an airplane ride.

I can't wait!

When Pop-Pop is not flying in his airplane, he visits me and reads me lots of stories. And sometimes when he reads to me, Pop-Pop changes some of the words in my books to silly words. He calls a "snowman" a "shnay man," and he changes the word "sleep" to "schluf." Pop-Pop makes me giggle and giggle some more.

And do you know who Grandpa Number Three is? He is my Baba, my mommy's daddy.

My mommy told me that Baba used to work as a mechanical engineer. I did not know what a mechanical engineer was. So Mommy told me that when he wasn't in his office, Baba visited schools, factories, and hospitals, helping to save energy all over the country.

Wow! Baba helped so many people.

One day, not so long ago, Mommy and Daddy told me that Baba's body stopped working and that he won't be coming back again.

I was very sad.

But they show me lots of pictures of Baba all the time. And the pictures help me remember how we played together and had so much fun.

When Baba used to visit me, he would pick me up, give me lots of hugs and kisses, and then put me all the way up on his shoulders.

I felt like I could touch the clouds in the sky.

And when Baba took me swimming at the beach, he lifted me over the waves. He was so strong.

We really had a super time!

Grampy will teach me how to play golf when I get bigger.

Pop-Pop is going to take me on an airplane ride.

And Baba will stay on my mind and in my heart forever and ever.

All my grandpas are the best. I am so lucky!